PICTURE HISTORY

MACHINES

IN HISTORY

Andrew Nahum

PICTURE HISTORY

First published in 1985 by
Wayland (Publishers) Limited
49 Lansdowne Place, Hove
East Sussex BN3 1HF, England

© Copyright 1985 Wayland (Publishers) Ltd

ISBN 0 85078 351 8

Series design by Behram Kapadia

Phototypeset by Eastern Counties Printers Limited,
Ely, Cambs.
Printed in Italy by G. Canale & C.S.p.A., Turin
Bound in the U.K. by The Pitman Press, Bath

Contents

Introduction

Have you ever thought how important machines are in our lives? Today almost everything we buy or use has been built, sorted, or packed by machine. This book was printed by machines, assembled and glued into its covers by a different machine, and packed for distribution by another. The paper it is printed on was made by machines too. Try to think of some things you use and touch every day which were *not* made or handled by machine — it will not be easy.

The Earliest Machines

Of course, life was not always like this. In very early times most articles were made by hand and most of the work was done by hand. But from the very beginning of settled civilization, people started to develop machines to ease the most laborious and repetitive tasks. The earliest devices would probably have included the hand mill for grinding corn, a wheel or chain of pots for raising water for irrigation, and the windlass for use in wells and mines.

Mechanical knowledge expanded during the period of classical Greek civilization (between 500 and 400 BC). The actions of the screw thread, the pulley, the lever and the wheel and axle were all described by Greek authors.

We also know that the Greeks could construct mechanisms with complex chains of gears.

The Romans were more practical in their use of machinery. They devised water wheels for powering flour mills, and for sawing timber, used screw presses for extracting olive oil, and produced various types of 'ballistic engines' (like giant catapults) for warfare.

The Industrial Revolution

The development of machines continued through the following centuries. However, from about 1750, starting in Britain, there was a tremendous growth in the use of machinery and the development of technology — a period that has been called 'The Industrial Revolution'.

Whether it was really a 'revolution' has been disputed, for machines were in common use and being improved before this, but the scale and speed of the change was quite new and it brought huge changes to living patterns.

People often ask if the benefits of machines are not outweighed by the problems they have brought. The question has no answer, for there was never any choice. Every ingenious smith or mechanic who was glad to find a better way to make a bolt, a spring, or an axle, in his daily work helped mechanical progress on its way. The history of human culture is written as much in its machines as in its literature.

8

The Seed Drill

Many of the machines shown in this book have been important in the process of *industrialization*. But industrialization depended on people having enough income to buy manufactured products. We can see today in the Third World that many people own virtually no manufactured articles. All their income is spent getting enough food.

Industrialization depended first of all on improvement in the methods of food production. Then, since people had grown more food in the locality than they needed to live, they could sell it to buy other things. Better methods also meant that fewer people were required to cultivate the land, and this released a pool of labour to man the new factories.

Increased Productivity

Since mankind first settled and started to farm people must have watched what grew well and tried their own ideas to improve crop yields. Even in Europe, during what, perhaps wrongly, are called the 'Dark Ages', better agricultural techniques started to improve the productivity of the land, and increase the amount grown *per* worker.

By many small steps, the methods used to win produce from the land improved, and it was natural that human ingenuity was used first of all for getting food. Probably the first 'machine' that most people in Northern Europe would be familiar with was the mill (wind or water powered) for grinding corn.

Jethro Tull

However, these machines were used in the farmyard, when the produce had been brought in. In the early eighteenth century Jethro Tull was a pioneer for taking machinery on to the land itself. He thought that if seeds were sowed in straight rows, rather than scattered in the traditional way, it would be easier to hoe the crop to keep it free from weeds that also compete for light and nourishment from the soil. His machine, shown in our picture, was horse-drawn, and as blades cut into the soil, a set of tubes fed seeds into the furrows they made at an even rate. It was called a seed drill.

Tull was not the first to sow in rows, or to think of using a machine. But he does seem to have been the first to design, build and use one. His improvements did not catch on everywhere straight away. About 80 years after his demonstration, a writer noted that there was not perhaps a drill, a horse hoe, or scarcely a horse rake in East Norfolk. However, Tull's theories, and the demonstration that machines could be used usefully on the land, had a real effect in persuading people to try the new methods.

9

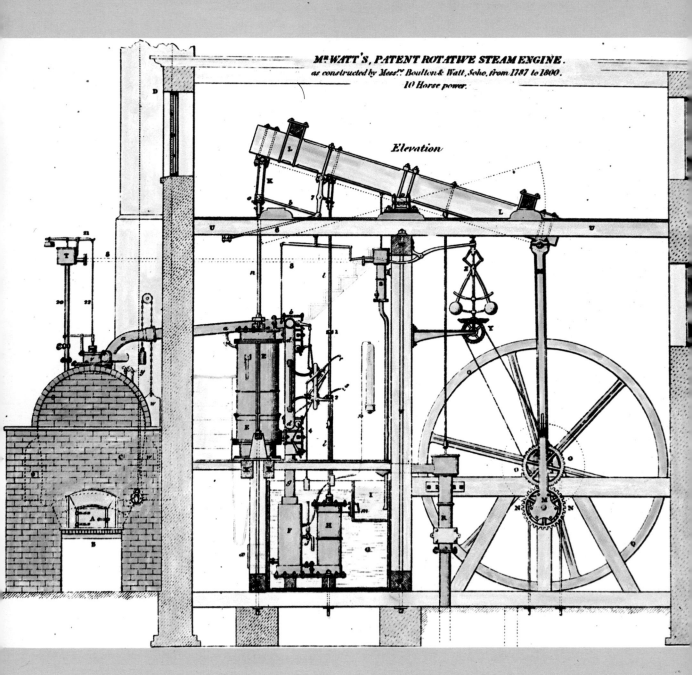

Mʳ WATT'S, PATENT ROTATIVE STEAM ENGINE.
as constructed by Messʳˢ Boulton & Watt, Soho, from 1787 to 1800.
10 Horse power.

Elevation

10

The Rotative Steam Engine

James Watt was an instrument maker, attached to the University of Glasgow, when he first began to think about steam power.

The 'condensing engine' had been invented by Thomas Newcomen in 1712. Throughout the eighteenth century, there was a growing demand for coal and metals, but the depth to which these resources could be mined was often limited by the risk of water flooding the mine workings. The Newcomen engine was the only practical way of pumping water from mines, and it spread rapidly through the industry.

Inefficient Engine

It was a model of the Newcomen engine, that Watt was asked to repair in 1763 that first directed his attention to steam power. The model would not run for more than a few strokes, and Watt was puzzled as to why it used so much steam. In the Newcomen engine, the cylinder was first filled with steam, and then a spray of cold water into the cylinder condensed the steam and created a partial vacuum, pulling the piston down for the working stroke.

Watt realized that the alternate heating and cooling was a source of inefficiency and devised a separate condenser. Watt's invention made a dramatic improvement to the efficiency of the steam engine, but his engine was more difficult to manufacture.

However, this was solved with the help of facilities provided by Matthew Boulton, a Birmingham industrialist and businessman, who went into partnership with Watt to build engines.

From 1776, the partners started supplying steam engines to mine owners. However, Boulton realized the great business potential of a steam engine that could produce rotary motion to drive the growing number of textile mills and factories.

Boulton wrote to Watt that 'the people in London, Manchester and Birmingham are *steam mill mad.*' Watt returned from the profitable Cornish pumping business to the Soho factory near Birmingham to start work on the project.

Rotary Power

The engine was still of the rocking beam type — like the pumping engine, but instead of driving a pump by simple up and down motion, it was adapted to drive a flywheel and give rotary power. From the engine, belts and shafts could run throughout a factory, and take the power to the various machines. Steam power helped to revolutionize industrial production, although water power continued to play an important part for many mills and factories.

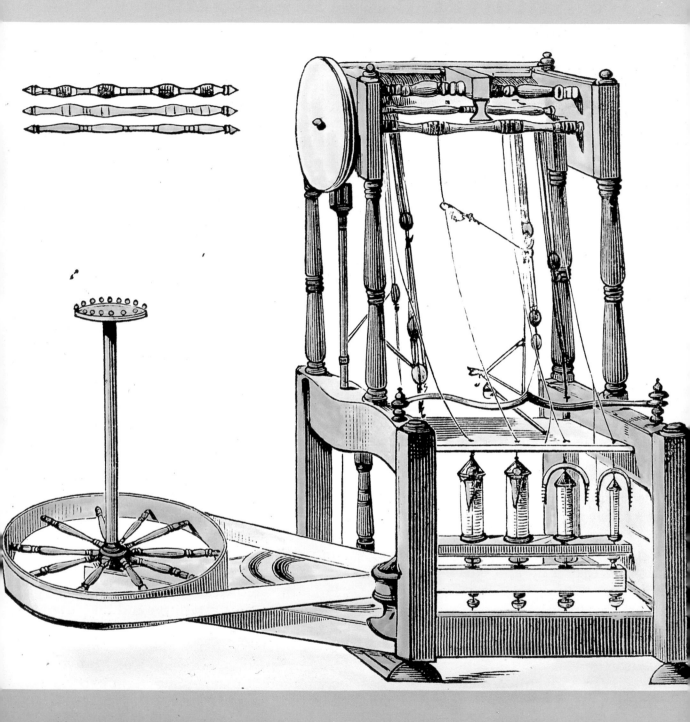

Arkwright's Spinning Engine

At the start of the Industrial Revolution, there was no real profession of 'engineer', and the people who developed important machines came from a variety of backgrounds. Richard Arkwright was working as a barber in Bolton when he became interested in developing a machine that would spin.

Advances in textile manufacturing led to the development of the factory system, and opened the way for the Industrial Revolution. There are two main reasons for this.

Increased Production

Firstly, after food, clothing is one of the fundamental necessities of life, so cheaper methods of textile production should repay the manufacturer with greater sales.

Secondly, the preparation and spinning of cotton and wool involved so much labour that any improvements in production methods would produce a tremendous saving in wage costs. Arkwright's water-powered spinning machines increased the amount of yarn one worker could produce several hundred times.

Arkwright patented his first machine in 1769. He used a series of rollers through which the thread passed. These rollers did the same job as the fingers of an experienced spinner, for each set ran a little faster than the ones before, drawing out the yarn progressively, and making it finer. From these rollers, the yarn ran to a U-shaped 'flyer' that rotated around a bobbin, twisting up the yarn and winding it on to the bobbin at the same time.

Arkwright did not invent the elements of this machine, but he had the idea of bringing them together. He designed factories where a single source of power (from a water wheel) was transmitted throughout the building, and worked all the various machines. He also devised machines for preparing the cotton before spinning (carding and drawing) and designed the system so that there was an efficient flow of material from one process to another.

Power Looms

Arkwright is probably more famous for his organization of the factory system than for his machinery, and for this reason he is thought of as one of the founders of the Industrial Revolution.

The improvements he made in spinning technology were copied widely, as was his form of industrial organization. The more rapid production of yarn also encouraged the eventual development of the power loom, which was a faster method of weaving and required a smaller labour force.

Brunel's Blockmaking Machines

'Mass' production is often considered to be an American invention, imported into Britain after the impression it had made at the Great Exhibition of 1851.

However, there were many European examples of mass production before this, and the Portsmouth blockmaking machinery, designed by Marc Isambard Brunel, was perhaps the most interesting. Brunel was a Frenchman, who emigrated after the revolution. For a time he settled in America and worked on various engineering projects there. One night at a dinner party, he heard of the high cost of the manufacture of pulley blocks for the British Navy, and set to thinking about the problem.

Building Blocks

Brunel had received a first class education in mathematics and engineering drawing, and in addition had spent six years on a French Navy ship, so he could fully understand the problem. A single warship would need about 1,000 pulley blocks (used for everything from handling sails and spars, to hauling out guns or loading stores), so the yearly expenditure for the whole navy was a considerable sum, as a pulley block was a fairly complex manufacturing task, with about eight parts and a shaped wooden body. Brunel started thinking about how they could be made by machine, and arrived in London in 1799 with his proposals.

Samuel Bentham, the man in charge of 'naval works', was impressed by Brunel's designs, and the great engineer, Henry Maudslay (see page 19) was commissioned to build them. Between 1802 and 1807 45 machines were installed at Portsmouth dockyard. They were built and designed so well that some were in use for over a century.

Woodworking machinery was not new — even before Brunel's scheme, contractors for naval pulley blocks were using some powered saws and other machinery (driven by horse mills or water). What was notable about Brunel's system was a well-thought-out arrangement of special-purpose machines, each designed to do one part of the job properly. There was still, inevitably, some hand work and fitting, but the machinery allowed an efficient and fairly continuous flow through the 'block mill'. The machine in our picture was used to shape the wooden pulley blocks.

Popular Attraction

The machinery was said to have paid for itself in four years. Brunel was paid £17,000, a figure based on one year's estimated cost saving. The machinery could produce about 1,400 blocks a day, and with a tenth of the former manpower requirements.

The Watch

Today nearly everybody in industrialized countries wears a watch. Even if you do not, you are seldom out of sight of a clock, on a building, in an office, or on a car's dashboard. Clocks regulate our life.

Gongs and Bells

In spite of the dominance of time, the actual origin of the clock is a technological mystery. We know that many ancient civilizations used the water clock, which measured time by the slow trickle of water from a container; and the sun dial was also useful (if there was sun!) but time measurement was very imprecise.

However, in communities, there would usually be some signal for telling the time. Perhaps gongs would beat to announce a court meeting, or a special bell might signal the end of the morning's work. The person who struck the signal would not know the time exactly — but the important thing was that everyone got the same message. The ringing of church bells before the service is probably today the last reminder of this clock-less age.

Mechanical clocks were probably developed in the monasteries of the Middle Ages. Not only did the monks in them meet to pray at many times during the day (and the night), but they often ran efficient farming communities. Work and prayer were regulated by the frequent ringing of bells, and it seems likely that the clock was developed to make this process automatic (the very word 'clock' means a bell in German, Dutch, and Old English).

The first mechanical clock we know about definitely was one built for Norwich Cathedral, around 1325. A famous clock was also started at St. Albans by Richard of Wallingford (who lived from 1292 to 1335), that took thirty years to build, and displayed much complicated astronomical information.

Miniaturization

The subsequent history of the time keeper was one of continuous improvement — and of miniaturization. By about 1550, spring-driven watches could be obtained which were small enough to carry, although we would not think them very accurate.

However as industry developed, and travel between places by coach became more and more regular there was an increasing need for timekeeping and timetables. Large clock and watchmaking trades grew up in most European countries. Our picture is an eighteenth-century advertisement for a watchmaker's shop. It shows a customer bringing his pocket watch in to be repaired.

18

The Whitworth Lathe

The lathe is often regarded as the basic machine tool, for it can be adapted to perform the functions of almost all the other types of tool. Shaping objects by cutting them in a lathe is called turning.

Very early lathes were spun by a cord wound round a spindle, and worked back and forth by a bow. This required an assistant to drive the bow, or else the turner would use one hand for this, and the other to direct the cutting tool.

In the Middle Ages, the lathe was improved by using a treadle and pole. A springy pole was mounted above the lathe, and from it a cord passed down, round the spindle, and then to a foot treadle. Now the turner could keep the lathe running by himself.

Need for Accurate Tools

The lathe developed further with the use of the 'slide-rest', a fixed mounting on which the cutting tool could be bolted.

As the Industrial Revolution gathered pace in the mid-nineteenth century, there was a growing demand for accurate machine tools. We have seen that the textile industry was among the first to be mechanized and re-organized on the factory system, and it was the requirement to build and service the complex textile machinery that stimulated the development of tool design.

Perhaps the pioneer of the modern type of all-metal industrial lathe was the master machine builder, Henry Maudslay. Previously wood had been used for the frames of industrial lathes, but he realized that rigidity was one of the keys to accuracy and made his in iron.

He also pioneered the screw-cutting lathe, in which the tool is moved evenly along the workpiece by a rotating 'lead screw' and so cuts a thread automatically. For his first screw-cutting lathe Maudslay had to mark out and cut his lead screw with special accuracy, for the performance of the lathe and all others that might be made using it depended critically on this part.

World-wide Fame

Joseph Whitworth had worked in Maudslay's shop. He subsequently returned to his native Manchester, and set up in business there in 1833. Maudslay and other engineers built not only machine tools, but also steam engines, textile machinery and many other products. Whitworth specialized solely in the manufacture of machine tools and workshop equipment, becoming the world's first specialist supplier. His efforts played a great part in the improvement of standards of working throughout the profession, and the accuracy of his products brought him world-wide fame.

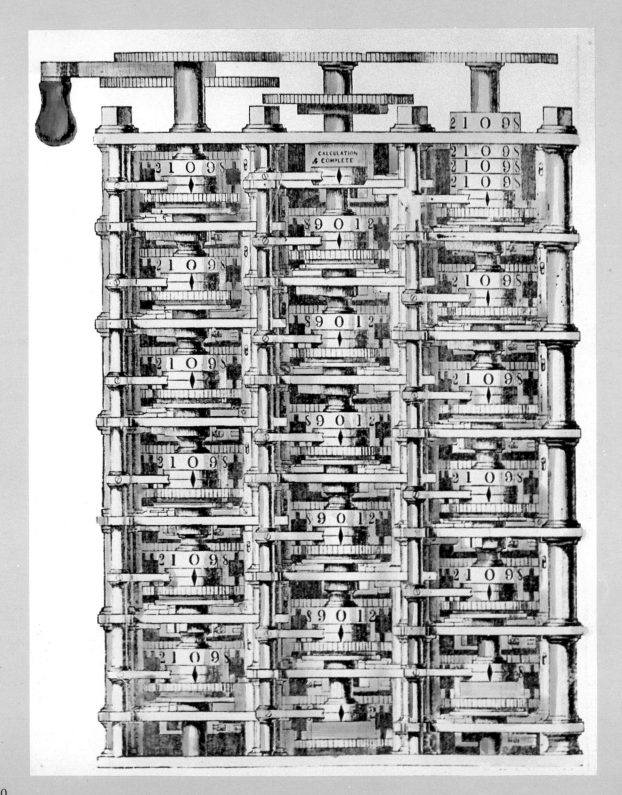

Babbage's Computing Engines

Charles Babbage was a 'man with a mania' — a noted nineteenth-century mathematician who, before the age of electronics, devoted much of his life to trying to build computing devices.

The first mechanical calculator was devised in the seventeenth century by Blaise Pascal, a French mathematician. It used a train of gears to add, subtract, and 'carry' numbers. Another mathematician, Gottfried Leibnitz also designed a machine in 1673. Thus, when Babbage began his experiments in about 1820, there was already a history of geared calculating machines.

A 'Difference Engine'

However, Babbage's plans went far beyond anything that had been conceived before. He proposed the construction of a 'Difference Engine': a complicated machine that would automatically calculate mathematical tables. It is shown in our picture.

Babbage was awarded a grant of £1,500 to develop the machine. If completed it would have calculated to 20 significant figures and weighed two tonnes. However there were many difficulties in building it, and the project was suspended in 1833.

Although the attempt to build the Difference Engine had indicated that Babbage's ideas were probably too far ahead of the technology of the day, work on the project had made him realize that, theoretically, a machine could be devised to perform any kind of computation, rather than a few specialized tasks. He then started the design of an even more ambitious machine which anticipated many features of the modern computer. It was to have a 'store', or memory, a 'mill' to perform the calculations (now it would be called a central processor) and an output section and printer.

Input Cards

Babbage also showed great ingenuity in the design of the input mechanism. He was not to know that punched cards would be the standard method of input when the age of electronic computing dawned, but he adapted the cards used in the Jacquard loom to enter numbers into the engine, and to direct the types of calculation that would be performed (the program). In a Jacquard loom, the cards control the weaving to produce patterned fabric.

Eventually, work on Babbage's second engine also had to stop, to his great disappointment, for a computer of the power and complexity he had envisaged could not be produced until the development of electronics. However his theoretical insights had been absolutely correct.

Trevithick's Steam Engine

Richard Trevithick was the son of a Cornish mine engineer and grew up working with Newcomen and Watt engines. By the age of 19 he was already holding responsible jobs in Cornish mines. The engines he worked with used the steam mainly to produce a partial vacuum below the piston. Atmospheric pressure acting above then forced the piston down — so they are called 'atmospheric' engines.

This system required modest steam pressure only, and suited the rivetted, blacksmith-made boilers that were in use. However the great power of steam under pressure was realized, and various attempts were made to use it to increase the power of engines.

Small but Powerful

From about 1798 Trevithick built a series of high-pressure winding engines in Cornwall. He demonstrated that the use of high-pressure steam made it possible to build small engines that were as powerful as the huge beam engines.

Trevithick had to design a boiler that would withstand a pressure ten times that of an atmospheric engine's. He devised one with an internal firebox, surrounded by the water, and a U-shaped flue that returned to the front of the boiler before joining the chimney. By the standards of the day, it was an excellent design for extracting maximum heat from the fuel, and Trevithick also located the working cylinder inside the boiler to minimize heat wasted.

Critics claimed that high-pressure steam was dangerous, and a boiler explosion of a Trevithick engine at Greenwich in 1803 was naturally used by other builders to cast doubt on their safety. However, by 1804, nearly 50 of these efficient small engines had been bought.

Steam Locomotive

Trevithick realized that he had devised an engine that was compact and light enough to make a self-propelled vehicle possible, and made several experiments with steam road carriages with varying success. In 1809, he provoked tremendous interest by bringing his locomotive 'Catch-me-who-can' (shown in our picture) to London. Spectators paid a shilling to see it and ride on the carriage it pulled. Though Trevithick did not continue to develop steam railway engineering, he showed it was possible, and helped it to come about. He also showed the increasing variety of applications that the steam engine could be put to. He showed too that the power of the steam engine could be vastly increased and this development continued throughout the nineteenth century in factories, ships and locomotives.

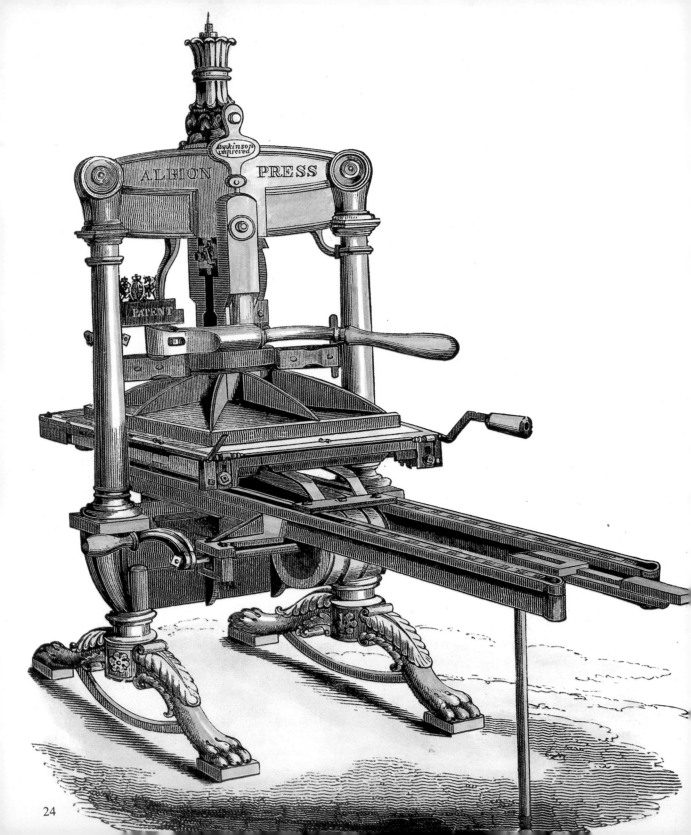

ALBION PRESS

Hopkinson improved

PATENT

The Albion Press

In the development of our industrial culture, better methods of communication have been just as important as improvements in manufacturing and machines.

When books were copied by hand in the Middle Ages, they were rare and expensive, and were owned mostly by religious institutions or monarchs and nobles. In AD 1300, the library of the French King held only 400 titles (although the Islamic library of Cordoba, in Spain, had 600,000).

Invention of Metal Type

If 'knowledge is power', this concentration of books shows where power lay. The development of printing was a crucial step in social development.

Printing had been known for a long time in China and perhaps reports of it encouraged people in Europe to experiment. What made the process really practical was the invention of metal type — blocks of a lead-tin alloy, one block for each letter. These could be assembled into a wooden frame to print a complete page, inked, and a wooden screw press (already a well-known device) used to press the type firmly against the paper.

The combination of these ideas is generally credited to Johann Gutenberg, of Mainz in Germany, who produced the first printed books in Europe in about 1450.

Demand for books grew steadily, but in the nineteenth century, with the spread of interest in education and 'self help', it accelerated even more. The process of printing had changed little in principle from Gutenberg's day, although the press was usually made of iron to exert more pressure, and give a stronger impression.

Widely Used

One of the most widely used iron presses was the Albion, invented in 1823, and shown in our picture. Though already superseded technically by machine-driven presses, hand presses like the Albion were popular with small printers and for proof printing type that would subsequently be printed by machine.

One difference (apart from the superior construction) between the Albion and presses of the Middle Ages, is the method of applying pressure to the paper. For faster action the screw thread is replaced by a sliding steel wedge, and a system of levers.

However, although the tools and the materials were better, the nineteenth-century printer was still performing essentially the same tasks as Gutenberg did in the fifteenth century — setting movable type by hand, inking the assembled frames, and pressing on to paper, one sheet at a time.

The Sewing Machine

As we have seen, the development of spinning and weaving by machine made a tremendous reduction in the labour required (and the cost) of making textiles. However, it was still time-consuming to 'make up' the cloth into garments. The well-off could afford to have clothes made for them by tailors, but most families made their own.

This was generally done by the women, and they would have had to spend a very high proportion of their time making and mending clothes.

Angry Tailors

Various people tried to make a machine that would take some of the work out of hand sewing. In France, Barthelemy Thimonnier (shown in our picture) devised a wooden machine in 1830, and set up 80 of them to make clothing for the army. Unfortunately, his workshop was broken up by some enraged and worried tailors.

In 1845, an American, Elias Howe, devised a machine that had most of the main features of a machine that had a practical use. It had an 'eye pointed' needle that carried thread at the pointed end, and since the needle could not pass right through the cloth, as in hand sewing, there was a shuttle on the other side with its own supply of thread. Stitches were made by these two threads inter-linking.

Elias Howe had a long struggle to get his machine accepted. People saw that it could sew, but they could not see the point of it. Howe thought that Britain, the pioneer of machine development, was the place to show his invention and travelled there to try and sell it. He had little success, and sold the manufacturing rights for only £250. He became so short of money that he had to sell a prototype of his machine for £5, to return to the USA.

When he got back, he found that the sewing-machine business had taken off. Several versions were on the market, and he had to undertake a series of court actions to obtain royalty payments from the manufacturers who were using the ideas that he had patented.

Singer Sewing Machine

One of these was Isaac Merritt Singer. A penniless theatre manager, Singer had made some improvements to a sewing-machine design, and founded a world-wide company.

The sewing machine made possible the production of cheap mass-produced clothes (Levi jeans are an early example). It was also so useful to poorer rural families in America that the Singer company invented the 'hire purchase' system to enable them to buy it.

28

Whitworth Measuring Machine

During the eighteenth and nineteenth centuries, the engineers who built the new machines, and the tools that made them, had to make sure that they were made with greater precision, for the accuracy of the original machine tools determined that of the subsequent 'generations' of machines they built.

Screw Threads

The pioneering engineers devised many ingenious methods to check and refine the accuracy of their own tools and measuring equipment. Screw threads are not just important as fastenings — nuts and bolts — holding parts together. They play a crucial part in the operation of most machinery, controlling the movement accurately of one component relative to another. For example, in a lathe, screw threads control all the movements of the cutting tool against the workpiece.

An accurate screw thread also makes it possible to build a sensitive measuring instrument. In about 1805, Henry Maudslay built a bench micrometer (or measuring machine) as the ultimate standard for his engineering workshop. The heart of the device was a screw that he had specially cut, with a spiral of 100 threads per inch. The wheel which rotated the screw was itself graduated into 100 divisions, so a movement of one division advanced a jaw of the machine by 1/10,000 of an inch. The idea of using a screw thread to measure was not new. James Watt, among others, had built a micrometer around 1770. However Maudslay devoted more attention than anyone before to perfecting its accuracy.

Joseph Whitworth (shown in our picture) continued this attention to screw threads, and his 'Whitworth' threads were the first unified national system — before this, most machine builders had their own ranges. He also carried on the development of the micrometer, and in 1856 produced the Whitworth 'Millionth Measuring Machine', capable of detecting length differences of one-millionth of an inch. He also produced a standard workshop measuring machine that was sold to engineers and workshops.

Accurate Parts

Before the era of exact measurement, skilled craftsmen could fit parts individually to the highest accuracy. This was how chronometers, scientific instruments and guns were made. But since this had to be done individually, and by hand, it was time consuming and expensive. Micrometer measurement made it possible to produce parts repeatedly. This saved time and labour when the complete machine was assembled from these components.

The Otto Gas Engine

As steam power developed, the demand for engines became more and more widespread. Small businesses desperately needed a small, efficient power source, but the steam engine was not really suitable. The smaller the steam engine, the greater is the waste of heat.

Etienne Lenoir's Engine

However, engineers began to think that burning fuel *internally* in the working cylinder itself, rather than externally to heat a boiler should reduce the amount of heat that 'escapes' and is wasted. Inventors tried burning coal gas in engines which looked often like little modified steam engines. The use of gas for lighting was spreading and the availability of this fuel helped the development of the gas engine. The first one to go into regular production was devised by the French inventor and engineer, Etienne Lenoir, in 1860.

Nicholaus August Otto was to become famous in internal combustion engineering, but when he first heard of the Lenoir engine, he was a travelling salesman trading in groceries and kitchenware near Cologne. However, he thought continually about mechanical problems, and built prototypes with the help of a local machinist. Otto was among the first experimenters to realize that compression of the gas-air mixture gave a much more powerful stroke when ignited. But at first he thought this great power would break up an engine. He therefore designed the type shown in our picture opposite.

Like the Lenoir, it operated without pre-compression. The initial movement of the piston draws the gas-air mixture into the cylinder, which is then ignited. Thus a single stroke of the piston is used to do two jobs — to bring in mixture, and to develop power. In this Otto engine, the upward motion of the piston is converted to rotary motion by a ratchet gear.

The Four-Stroke Engine

However, Otto returned to the idea of compression and, in 1876, devised an engine running on a four-stroke or 'Otto' cycle. Otto arranged for a complete stroke of the piston to draw the mixture in. The return stroke then compressed it. Ignition occurred, provoking the power stroke, and burnt gas was exhausted on the return. Thus four movements of the piston are required to perform all the functions.

Internal combustion engines soon came to run on fuels other than gas, and the petrol or 'gasolene' motor made the motor car a practical possibility. Otto's four-stroke cycle forms the basis of the majority of engines used today for cars, commercial vehicles and motorcycles.

The Telephone

During the nineteenth century, a new invention, the electric telegraph, spread rapidly. The telegraph network often developed hand in hand with the growing railway network, for the transmission lines could be set up alongside the track. In 1866, the first successful cable was laid under the Atlantic Ocean, from Britain to America, and soon, almost all the major cities of the world were linked.

However, sending messages by telegraph had one drawback: it transmitted them in the form of relatively slow pulses of electric current, so messages had to be spelt out laboriously by a trained operator in code — Morse code was the most widely used one.

Alexander Graham Bell

The telephone arose out of a desire to improve on this system, and to find a way of transmitting and receiving normal speech. As so often happens in the history of inventions, a similar idea may spring up in several minds at the same time, for Alexander Graham Bell beat a rival inventor to the patent office by only three hours when he went to register his telephone mechanism in 1876.

Bell was a teacher of the deaf, which must have given him an interest in sound and speech transmission. He was also a prolific inventor. He had been experimenting with sending tones of different pitch down telegraph lines, for he was trying to find a way to send a number of messages at the same time.

Transmitting these musical tones made him realize that he could perhaps also transmit a human voice. He devised a magnetic microphone earpiece and the first words transmitted over his system are said to have been to his assistant: 'Mr Watson, come here, I want you.'

The invention (shown in our picture) was the basis of a worldwide industry, and spread with remarkable speed. In 1878, the world's first telephone exchange opened in Hartford, Connecticut. London got one in the following year. By 1880, 50,000 telephones had been installed in American homes and offices.

Data Transmission

In the past few years, it has been realized that the telephone network is a unique world resource, for it reaches almost everywhere, and it has many more uses than just enabling two people to talk to one another. It can carry many other kinds of information. Data can be transmitted on phone lines as a stream of coded bleeps. Various devices can be used which communicate through a phone link; important documents or even photographs can be transmitted, and reproduced at the other end.

The Typewriter

The typewriter was one of those devices that inventors just *would* keep coming up with, long before the usefulness of a 'writing machine' was appreciated.

The first patented design dates from 1714, but it was during the mechanically minded nineteenth century that designs really proliferated. Many different schemes were tried for the printing mechanism, for inking the type, and for the layout of the keys.

Pitman's Shorthand

At first, the attractions of replacing a steel pen, costing a penny, by a machine that cost £20 were doubtful; but, in America towards the end of the nineteenth century, the typewriter began to be appreciated for business work. The clarity of the text was obviously superior, and when typewriting skill was combined with a knowledge of shorthand, the process became quicker than 'pen drudgery'.

In 1873, E. Remington and Sons signed a contract to manufacture typewriters to the design of C. L. Sholes (our picture shows one of his typewriters being used by a typist in 1872) and C. Glidden. This machine has been called the first practical typewriter, and as small arms manufacturers, the Remington company were competent to make a good job of the mechanism.

However, it is noteworthy that at the American Centennial Exposition of 1876, the Remington machine created little interest — though the Bell telephone, also on show, got world-wide attention. But interest gradually accelerated. In 1881, the New York City YWCA bought six Remington machines and began giving typing classes. By 1900 the yearly sales of typewriters in the USA was estimated at 7 million dollars and there were many thousands of typists.

Computer Technology

Many changes have occurred recently to the typewriter, for example the 'daisy wheel' to strike letters. However the most interesting feature is the integration of the typewriter into a computer data system. The typewriter can now also be an automatic printer for a word processor, or an input keyboard. Portable 'typewriters' are available that are so small that they are no thicker than a paperback book. They can type 'hard' copy, or store the text until it can be fed into a word-processing computer.

The division between data processing and a mechanical writing machine has become blurred, and the typewriter is becoming increasingly flexible. Future generations will need keyboard skills in the same way that everyone now needs to know how to use a pen.

Lilienthal's Glider

For centuries mankind had speculated that it might be possible to fly. After all, the graceful flight of the birds seemed to suggest that it should be possible.

Balloons and Gliders

However, by the seventeenth century, scientists like Robert Hooke, were publishing their conclusion that human muscles were too weak to allow bird-like flight, and this helped to discourage determined enthusiasts. However, the invention of the hot-air balloon in 1783 (quickly followed by the hydrogen balloon) showed that man really could travel through the air with the help of the right kind of technology.

A Yorkshire baronet, Sir George Cayley, was probably the first person to think seriously about what was needed to build a stable aircraft. In 1804, he built a successful 5 foot (1.5 metre) long model glider with a wing and a separate tailplane. The angle of the tailplane could be adjusted and a movable weight controlled the position of the centre of gravity. He also built full-size gliders, one of which is said to have carried his coachman across a valley.

Many models from various inventors followed Cayley's, continuing to remind people that heavier-than-air craft could fly, but it was not until 1890 that an aircraft was built that could carry a human being repeatedly and with reasonable safety. This was the work of Otto Lilienthal, a German who carried out most of his experiments near Berlin.

Lilienthal had had a thorough technical education, and had just finished training as a mechanical engineer when he started to build his aircraft. These were hang-gliders and he controlled them by swinging his body to shift weight in the desired direction. He had realized a crucial fact — it was not sufficient to design a machine that would fly in perfect conditions: it was also necessary to learn *how* to fly. Lilienthal set himself to master the gusts and turbulence that would be encountered.

Experienced Airman

He made some 2,500 flights, jumping off hills into the wind. He even had an artificial 50 foot (15 metre) hill made near Berlin for short tests, with a shed on top to store his aircraft. His experiments made him by far the most experienced airman of his day and his published accounts were of tremendous value to other pioneers—particularly the Wright brothers in America. Our picture shows Lilienthal almost coming to grief in 1894 when an attempt to fly from a tower in Frankfurt went disastrously wrong.

He was killed while soaring in 1896, when a gust of wind stalled his glider.

The Linotype Machine

The development of machine-driven printing presses in the early nineteenth century helped speed up the output of printed material.

However, this development did nothing to speed up the labour of setting the type. It was still necessary for the compositor to set each word and line, letter by letter, selecting each letter by hand, until all the text was set.

Ottmar Merganthaler

Obviously the next improvement in printing was to find a way of setting the type by machine. Some inventors thought of devices where pressing letters on a keyboard would bring up each piece of type as required. Various problems result from this approach. In particular, breaking down the set type after printing and sorting it out to refill the storage compartments of the machine was still as time consuming as ever.

The problem was solved by devising a machine that would cast complete lines of text from molten type metal. In Ottmar Merganthaler's 'Linotype' machine, the operator uses a keyboard rather like a typewriter to assemble a line. Pressing the keys lines up 'matrices' (moulds for the letters), and when a line is completed and spaced to the operator's satisfaction, the molten type metal is run into the assembled mould.

The 'slugs' of type that are produced have to be assembled individually to form the columns and the pages, but this is relatively simple, compared with traditional typesetting. Type metal is expensive, but it has a relatively low melting point, so after printing, it is simply returned to the Linotype machine and melted down and re-used indefinitely. Our picture shows compositors at a printers working on Linotype machines in 1889.

Merganthaler was a German, working in America, and the first use of his invention was on the *New York Tribune* in 1886. As with machine printing, *The Times* also pioneered this invention in Britain, a few years later.

'Hot Metal'

Most book and magazine printing today uses a combination of computer and photographic technology for typesetting. However photographic materials are not particularly cheap, and are not re-useable like type metal. Linotype machines are a fast method of setting type — something that is important on a daily paper with tight deadlines. Many are in use world-wide, and most Fleet Street papers still work with 'hot metal' — the name for printing by Linotype machine, derived from the casting of the 'slugs' from molten type metal.

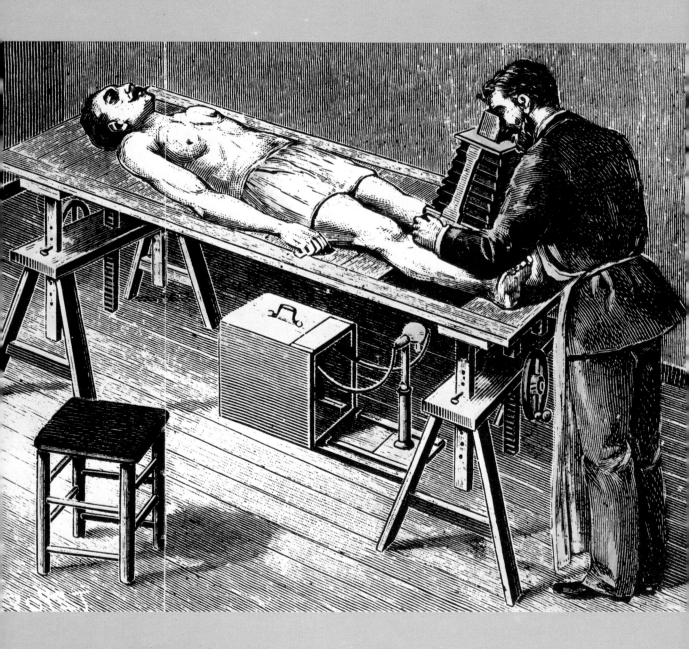

The X-Ray Machine

Towards the end of the nineteenth century, various physicists were investigating the flow of electricity through glass tubes filled with a gas at a low pressure. They were intrigued by various types of light and patterns developed in the tubes—'neon' lights are an example of this phenomenon.

Penetrating Rays

In 1895, Wilhelm Röntgen, Professor of Physics at Würzburg University in Germany, was experimenting with these 'discharge' tubes when he realized that some form of ray was penetrating the walls of the tube, for crystals of a fluorescent salt nearby began to glow.

Röntgen then spent seven weeks of intense work exploring the properties of the new rays. He found that they would pass through substances, like wood and living tissue, and would also create an image on photographic plates. For a report to the Physical Medical Society of Würzburg, he prepared various photographs, including one of a set of laboratory weights inside a closed box, another of the bones of his own hand. This particular picture caused a sensation, and his results were published in Britain less than a month after the initial announcement.

Röntgen called the emissions X-rays, because he did not know what they were, and this name has stuck. However, it was discovered that they were produced when a beam of electrons flowing in the discharge tube hit a solid object, and that they were a form of electromagnetic radiation, similar to radio waves and to light.

The medical profession was quick to realize how useful the new discovery would be. It was used almost immediately to show broken bones and bullets inside bodies. In 1896, commercial X-ray equipment for the medical profession was produced in America. It was also realized that X-rays were useful in treating malignant tumours, and this has become a standard method for cancer therapy.

Industrial Importance

X-rays have also become an important industrial and scientific tool.

A technique, called X-ray diffraction, has been important in biological research, for it gives clues about the structure of proteins and other substances. The images produced are not representations of the actual structure, like the picture of Röntgen's hand (because molecules are too small to be revealed in this way) but they show patterns which are created by the structure of the molecules and can be interpreted by skilled analysts.

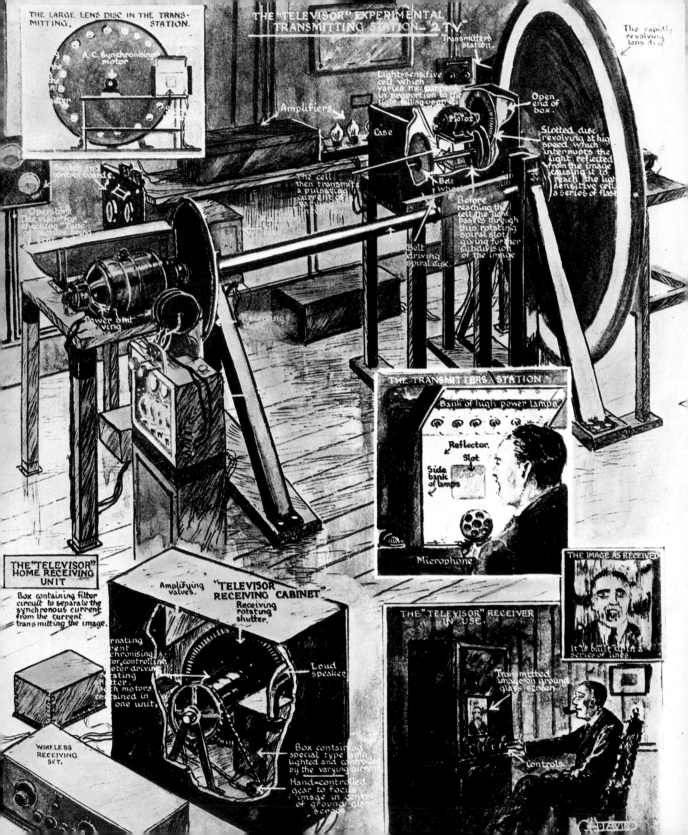

THE "TELEVISOR" EXPERIMENTAL TRANSMITTING STATION — "2 TV"

THE LARGE LENS DISC IN THE TRANSMITTING STATION.

A.C. synchronising motor

The rapidly revolving lens disc

Transmitters station

Light-sensitive cell which varies the current in proportion to the light falling upon it

Amplifiers

Case

Motor

Open end of box

Slotted disc revolving at high speed which interrupts the light reflected from the image causing it to reach the light sensitive cell a series of flashes

The cell then transmits a pulsating current of varying

Belt wheel

Switch and control board

Before reaching the cell the light passes through this rotating spiral slot giving further subdivision of the image

Operators Television for checking "Tune of picture" sent

Belt driving Spiral disc

Power Unit driving

Receiving

THE TRANSMITTERS STATION.

Bank of high power lamps

Reflector
Slot

Side bank of lamps

Microphone

THE IMAGE AS RECEIVED.

It is built up in a series of lines

THE "TELEVISOR" HOME RECEIVING UNIT

Box containing filter circuit to separate the synchronous current from the current transmitting the image.

Amplifying valves.

"TELEVISOR" RECEIVING CABINET.

Receiving rotating shutter.

Alternating current synchronising motor, controlling motor driving rotating shutter. Both motors contained in one unit.

Loud speaker

THE "TELEVISOR" RECEIVER IN USE.

Transmitted image on ground glass screen

Controls

Box containing special type lamp lighted and controlled by the varying current

Hand-controlled gear to focus image in centre of ground glass screen

WIRELESS RECEIVING SET.

G. A. DAVIS

Television

The first regular radio service in Britain began in 1922. It was transmitted by the Marconi company, and was limited to half an hour a week! The public interest created by these transmissions led to the creation of a national broadcasting company, the BBC (British Broadcasting Company) to provide a regular service.

Transmitting Pictures

But before the radio network had even become established, some far-sighted inventors were predicting that it would be possible to transmit moving pictures. One such person was John Logie Baird, and in 1922 he gave a demonstration of picture transmission in Selfridges department store in London.

To transmit a two-dimensional image, it is necessary to convert it into a single stream of information. The image is scanned in regular lines, and the brightness of the image measured at each point along the line. This process is repeated rapidly until the whole picture has been covered, and the scanning starts again. From the coded signals produced by this process, a suitable receiver can reconstruct a version of the original image.

To perform this scanning, Baird used a mechanical, rotating-disc system. This was relatively simple to construct, but the results were crude. Our picture is a page from the *The Illustrated London News* of September 1926, and shows the complicated apparatus used by Baird to transmit pictures. The BBC transmitted Baird television in 1929 as an experiment, outside normal broadcasting hours. Although many enthusiasts were intrigued to receive pictures on special equipment that was often home-built from kits, they had little value as popular entertainment. The flickering picture had poor clarity.

Seeing in the Dark

Baird did not persist in improving his system at the time. He was brimming with ideas and suggested a transatlantic TV service, 'Phonovision' (TV on gramophone discs) and 'Noctovision' — a device for seeing in the dark! The result was that his group of engineers was overtaken by the EMI company, which replaced mechanical scanning with an electronic beam system, scanning the image formed inside the camera. This enabled the EMI-Marconi company to offer a 405-line picture which was really sharp compared to the 250-line image the Baird system was now working at. Neither could the Baird equipment provide outside broadcasts. The BBC gave both systems a trial for a few months, but in 1937 announced it would use the EMI-Marconi one.

The Personal Camera

In 1839, photographs taken by Louis Daguerre were first shown at a meeting in Paris. The meeting was historic, and attracted great interest, for the possibility of recording permanent images had been discussed for many years.

'Camera Obscura'

The essential elements of the invention were already in existence, for the 'camera obscura' (Latin for 'dark room') in which an image could be focused and viewed inside a chamber had been known for centuries. Light-sensitive chemicals (particularly silver compounds) were also known.

Daguerre's process was popular, but each view was a 'one-off', and could not be copied. The images were also very delicate. An English photographer W. H. Fox Talbot, working at the same time, devised another kind of process, in which a 'negative' image was first formed in the camera, and this was then used to print the final 'positive' image — like the system still generally used.

For several years, photography remained an occupation for professionals or enthusiasts, for the photographer had to be prepared to do a considerable amount of preparation of chemicals and of plates. Furthermore, the equipment was bulky and heavy.

The invention of roll film changed this. Previously, the light-sensitive coating of chemicals was carried on glass plates which were inserted individually in the camera for each shot.

By the turn of the century there was a trend to make smaller cameras, like the one in our picture, that were accurate and suitable for professional use. The most famous of these was the Leica. Oskar Barnack, a designer at the well-known German optical firm of Ernst Leitz, enjoyed cross-country walking and taking landscape photographs. However, he resented the size and weight of the cameras that were needed for good results and decided to make his own small precision camera.

35mm Leica Camera

Leitz decided to put Barnack's prototype into production as the Leica (abbreviation for LEitz CAmera) in 1925. Though the Leitz Company had never made a camera for general sale, it had the expertise to succeed, and the camera quickly became popular with photo-journalists, explorers and artistic photographers.

Today the 35mm camera is probably the most popular type. Leica pioneered the idea, and also the 'system' concept, by which a large range of lenses and accessories could be bought for special uses, which would all fit the basic camera body.

The Jet Engine

The first aeroplanes flew with engines that had been designed for cars, motorcycles, and even speedboats. However special aircraft piston engines were soon developed.

During the 1920's and 1930's, the piston aero-engine became more reliable and powerful and aircraft speeds rose.

Doubt Among Experts

However, a RAF pilot, Flight-Lieutenant Frank Whittle believed that a light-weight gas turbine could be built for jet propulsion, and would enable aircraft to fly at even greater speeds and height. He put his proposals to the British Air Ministry. Although there was great doubt among experts about whether such an engine could be successful, the Ministry sent him to Cambridge University for further study and also allowed him to work part-time at Power Jets, a company he founded.

In a piston engine, a mixture of air and fuel is compressed by the piston working in its close-fitting cylinder. When this compressed mixture is ignited, the burning gas expands and drives the piston down. The gas turbine works in a similar way, but compression, combustion, and expansion are all continuous, so potentially, the engine can work at a far higher rate.

To build a practical gas turbine for aircraft use, it was necessary to develop a very efficient rotary compressor, a new combustion system that would work in the fast-moving air, and an efficient turbine that could also stand the continuous high temperature. These developments were all difficult and the Power Jets team worked for three years before they could make an engine run properly on the ground.

But this success encouraged the Air Ministry to order another experimental engine, the W1, for flight tests. This first flew in an aircraft on 15 May 1941.

Passenger Jets

It was originally thought that the high fuel consumption of the jet would mean that it was suitable only for military uses. However, development was more rapid than generally expected, and perhaps the most surprising feature of the 'jet story' was the speed with which it replaced the piston engine in almost every sphere of aviation (except light aircraft). The development of piston aero-engines virtually stopped after the end of the Second World War, and in 1952 the first passenger jet service was started by the British De Havilland Comet aircraft, one of which is shown in our picture. Today, virtually all transport aircraft and helicopters are powered by gas-turbine engines.

The Minicomputer

The development of electronic computing has probably been the greatest single technological change since the beginning of this century. Machine tools have become more accurate; and cars faster and cheaper, but most machinery has improved by gentle evolution.

However, where computer control has been coupled to existing machinery, new types of machine have emerged with far more power and capability. For example, a milling machine can cut metal accurately, as long as it has a skilled machinist to operate it. A computer-controlled milling machine can shape parts all day and night, by itself.

Colossus and ENIAC

We have seen that Babbage's ideas for a computer were too advanced for the nineteenth-century technology of gears and levers. However, in the 1930's various experimenters started to develop powerful calculators with a mixture of mechanical and electrical components (these were 'relays'). As so often happens, war is a tremendous spur to technological progress.

During the Second World War, Colossus was developed in Britain for cracking enemy codes; while ENIAC (Electronic Numeral Integrator and Calculator) was developed in the USA. This machine contained 18,000 electronic valves and cost $500,000.

These early computers were huge, but the post-war invention of the transistor, as a replacement for the bulky thermionic valve, made it possible to reduce the size of the machines, though they were still very big.

Small but Powerful

However the reduction in cost of electronic components, and increasing miniaturization (coming from 'integrated circuit' technology) made it possible to provide more and more power in a smaller machine. The Digital PDP 8 (shown in our picture), launched in 1965, was the first machine that was built with size, rather than pure computing capacity as the main consideration. It was an enormous success, and over 50,000 were built.

The minicomputer opened up many new applications for data processing, and control. The section on industrial robots points out that the development of the robot relies predominantly on computer control, and minicomputers were also powerful enough to be used to control industrial processes. For example, at Austin-Rover's Longbridge plant, PDP 11 minicomputers (the successor to the PDP 8) run the parts stores, and control the movement of cars down the production line.

The Combine Harvester

Throughout the nineteenth century, people became increasingly 'machine-minded', and it was inevitable that they would soon turn to devising machines for agricultural processes. However, machinery worked usually in factories, with skilled people to maintain it, and did a specific task on one type of raw material. The problem on farms was different, since the machines might receive little maintenance, and work in very varied conditions.

A Mechanical Reaper

In spite of this, there were many attempts to find new methods to harvest corn, since the process used a lot of labour and a deterioration in the weather during harvesting could result in losing much of the crop. Traditionally, the corn was cut by hand, by reapers with sickles, and then bound by others into bundles. These would be carried to the farmyard and threshed to break up the ears of corn, and separate the seeds (for that is the part we eat) out of the husks. The corn was then winnowed, to blow the light remains of the husks off the heavier grain.

The first mechanical reaper was invented by a Scottish church minister, Patrick Bell, in 1826. He used a row of teeth, parallel to the ground, with another set close above, moving from side to side and giving a scissors action. It was pushed by horses. A few years later, an American, Cyrus McCormick, produced a similar machine, but with a better cutting action.

Mechanical Thresher

However men still had to follow these machines and bind up the cut wheat. The next big improvement was for the machine to tie it in bundles itself. Some of these 'self-binding reapers' were still in use until quite recently. However the next step was to thresh the crop by machine too. Early mechanical threshers were steam driven. The sheaves were fed in, and the grain separated by a combination of 'beater drum' and various vibrating screens. An air blast from a fan also helped blow the chaff off the grain.

However, the crop still had to be taken to the threshing machine after harvesting. The next step was obviously to *combine* the threshing and reaping machines in one. Development was strongest in the great wheatfields of America, but as long as horses provided the power it was hardly practical. Up to 40 beasts were needed to pull some of these early machines. However, with the coming of the tractor, the combine harvester became a thoroughly useful device. The final step was to make it self-powered, like the one at work in our picture.

The Nuclear Reactor

Most power stations make electricity by burning coal or oil. They use the heat produced to raise steam which drives turbines to generate electricity. However nuclear power stations use a quite different type of energy which results from atomic 'fission' — the splitting of the atoms of the uranium fuel. Our picture shows the interior of the nuclear power station at Sizewell, on the Suffolk coast. The machine is used to raise and lower the rods of uranium fuel into the reactor.

Splitting the Atom

For many years, it seemed to chemists that atoms were the basic building blocks of matter. An atom of oxygen, for instance, was the smallest quantity of oxygen that could exist, and could not be divided any further. But with the dawn of the twentieth century, physicists began to follow clues that suggested that the atomic nucleus itself was composed of smaller particles.

During the First World War, Ernest Rutherford obtained evidence that the atom might, under some circumstances, be 'split'. As it became clear that atoms really could be split, other physicists began to suspect that the release of enormous amounts of energy might be possible.

Atomic power would not have come about so quickly, if it had not been for the rise of Hitler and the Nazi party in Germany. The persecution of anti-Nazi intellectuals forced many scientists to flee to America and Britain.

Manhattan Project

They feared that their former colleagues still in Germany might produce a 'super bomb' for Hitler, and they urged the American and British governments to start their own programme so that the Allies would not be powerless against it. The result was the Manhattan Project — at the time the most expensive scientific or military development ever undertaken. It proved that a controllable chain reaction could be produced in a reactor, and led on to the atomic bombs that were dropped on Japan at the end of the Second World War.

After the war, Britain pioneered the use of atomic power for electricity generation, by opening the Calder Hall power station in 1956. Other stations have been built since then, and today, nuclear power supplies about 13 per cent of British electricity. Partly, perhaps because it was the atomic bomb programme that stimulated its development, atomic power is always associated with the weapon. A power station cannot explode like a bomb though, for the fuel is less concentrated.

The Industrial Robot

One of the most dramatic features of current factory production has been the introduction of many industrial robots to do jobs that were previously done by people. Our picture shows robots in action on the Austin Metro production line at British Leyland's factory in Longbridge, Birmingham.

The sight of a car-body welding line, with a series of robots running through accurate and purposeful movements seems amazing to most people — and more than a little threatening. One reason for this is that the idea of man-made machines (or creatures) that could take on some life-like features and threaten their makers has been around for a long time as a literary myth.

Mechanical Models

In the eighteenth century, various inventors made incredibly life-like automata (mechanical models) driven by intricate clockwork mechanisms and which were celebrated curiosities in 'society'. One such was the Swiss, Pierre Jacquet-Droz. His model of a scholar at a desk would dip a pen into ink, shake the excess from the nib, put a hand on the paper to steady it and write the famous phrase of the philosopher Descartes *Cogito ergo sum* (I think therefore I exist). Mary Shelley visited this craftsman before she wrote her famous novel *Frankenstein* in 1818. The success of the book, and the many films on the same theme, show she had tapped (or perhaps created) a deeply felt fear of a machine with some human features.

Computer Control

However, modern-day robots are much less dramatic than those in fiction! They had their origin in 1956, when the inventor George Devol met the engineer Joseph Engelberger, who founded Unimation (from 'Universal Automation'). In 1983, Unimation led all suppliers with 24 per cent of the European market for industrial robots.

The mechanical part of industrial robots could have been built years before they began to be made. However, for robots to be useful as a tool, the development of modern computer technology was essential. Just to move the 'hand' from one place to another will require the precise movement of several different joints — a difficult control problem that is handled by the machine's own computer. It is this computer control, and the large information storage capacity ('memory') of modern computer systems that makes the robot so useful, for it can carry out a large number of different tasks, repeatedly and accurately, and also have the flexibility to be re-programmed.

Sources of Further Information

PLACES TO VISIT

The Science Museum, Exhibition Road, London SW7 exhibits many of the machines mentioned in this book. It also publishes leaflets and booklets on many of the subjects, and these are available in many libraries.

Here are some museums which demonstrate working machinery. This is a growth area and new projects are starting all the time, so this is by no means a complete list. For up-to-date information, refer to *Museums and Galleries in Great Britain and Ireland* (published by ABC Historic Publications, World Timetable Centre, Dunstable, Beds.) or *The Museums Yearbook* (published by The Museums Association, 34 Bloomsbury Way, London WC1). Both these publications should be available for consultation in your local reference library.

Abbeydale Industrial Hamlet, Abbeydale Road South, Sheffield. On several days a year, the museum uses its 18th- and 19th-century industrial equipment to simulate the activity of the site when it was used for forging scythe blades. It has working water wheels and a steam engine.

Bradford Industrial Museum, Moorside Mills, Bradford. This museum has many working textile machines.

The British Engineerium, Nevill Road, Hove, East Sussex. This has a beam engine which is in steam at specific times.

The Greater Manchester Museum of Science and Industry, Liverpool Road, Castlefield. This has special days when many machines (including a water wheel and steam and gas engines) can be seen working.

The Hunday National Tractor and Farm Museum, Newton Stocksfield, Northumberland. This has frequent demonstrations of its working exhibits.

The Ironbridge Gorge Museum Trust, Ironbridge, Telford, Salop. This has numerous working examples of early industrialization.

Kew Bridge Engines, Green Dragon Lane, Brentford, Middx. This shows beam engines in steam.

Leicestershire Museum of Technology, Abbey Pumping Station, Corporation Road, Leicester. This has working steam engines

BOOKS TO READ

and knitting machinery on special days. It also has a large collection of typewriters.

Museum of Science and Industry, Newhall Street, Birmingham. This has regular demonstrations of steam engines. It also has a good collection of machine tools.

North of England Open Air Museum, Beamish Hall, nr. Stanley, County Durham. This has many exhibits of working machinery, including mining machinery, printing, farming, and a steam train.

Quarrybank Mill, Styal, Cheshire. This has a large working, water-powered textile mill.

The Telecom Technology Showcase, 135 Queen Victoria Street, London EC4V 4AT. This has a number of working models of telecommunication technology.

Welsh Industrial and Maritime Museum, National Museum of Wales, Bute Street Docks, Cardiff. This museum demonstrates a number of steam, gas, oil and compressed-air engines.

Wheal Martin Museum, Carthew, St. Austell, Cornwall.

Burne, Gordon *Tools and Manufacturing* (Wayland, 1983)

Derry, T. K. & Williams, T. I. *A Short History of Technology* (Oxford University Press, 1960)

Evans, Christopher *The Mighty Micro* (Gollancz, 1979)

Forbes, R. J. *Man the Maker* (Constable, 1958)

Gilbert, K. R. *The Portsmouth Blockmaking Machinery* (Science Museum, 1965)

Litterick, Ian *Robots and Intelligent Machines* (Wayland, 1984)

Marsh, Peter *The Robot Age* (Abacus, 1982)

Marsh, Peter *The Silicon Chip Book* (Abacus, 1981)

Pacey, Arnold *The Maze of Ingenuity* (Allen Lane, 1974)

Rawson, Christopher *How Machines Work* (Usborne, 1976)

Strandh, Sigvard *Machines — An Illustrated History* (Mitchell Beazley, 1979)

The World of Machines (Macmillan, 1980)

Glossary

Compact: Closely packed or fitted together.

Condense: To turn a gas into a liquid, as in condensing steam by cooling to form water.

Dark Ages: The period in European history from about the late 5th century AD to about 1000 AD.

Data: Information.

Device: An invention.

Efficient: When referring to a machine, it means one that works without wasting a lot of energy. A machine that wastes energy is described as 'inefficient'.

Fluorescent: Something that emits light.

Fundamental: Something that is essential.

Hire purchase: Paying off the total price of something in small amounts, over a period of several years.

Industrialization: To develop industry on a large scale in a country or a region of a country.

Industrial Revolution: The period in the 18th and 19th centuries during which Britain changed from being mainly a farming country to an industrial and manufacturing one.

Ingenious: Skilfully designed or thought out, as in 'an ingenious machine'; or skilful in inventing, as in 'an ingenious person'.

Ingenuity: Cleverness.

Lathe: A machine for turning and shaping articles of wood, metal, etc.

Mania: A lot of enthusiasm or desire for something, such as having a 'mania' for football.

Mass production: The production of very large quantities of articles by machine to exactly the same pattern.

Middle Ages: The period in European history from the 11th to the 15th centuries.

Miniaturization: To make things on a very small scale.

Monastery: A building where monks live.

Patent: A legal document giving one person or a firm the sole right to make or sell a new invention.

Phenomenon: An unusual or remarkable event.

Pioneer: A person who invents or discovers something ahead of anyone else.

Pitch: The level of a musical note, in terms of being high or low.

Prolific: Very productive.

Prototype: The first of something, such as a car, from which successive models are copied.

Regulate: To control.

Royalty payment: Payment to an inventor who has patented the development of a machine for every machine that someone else builds and sells.

Stall: When an aircraft's speed drops below the speed necessary to keep it in the air.

Technology: The branches of science which have practical uses.

Third World: The poor, underdeveloped countries of the world.

Treadle: A part of a machine moved by the feet.

Vacuum: A space from which air and gas have been removed.

Windlass: A winch.

Acknowledgements and Sources of Pictures

cover Nasmyth's steam hammer. (Mary Evans Picture Library)

page 8 A mural of Jethro Tull and his seed drill, painted in the 1950's. (The Science Museum)

page 10 James Watt's 10 horsepower steam engine; hand-tinted for this book. (The Science Museum)

page 12 An eighteenth-century drawing of Arkwright's spinning machine; hand-tinted for this book. (Mary Evans Picture Library)

page 14 The shaping machine, part of Marc Isambard Brunel's machinery for making naval pulley blocks in Portsmouth dockyard; tinted for this book. (Ann Ronan Picture Library)

page 16 An eighteenth-century engraving; hand-tinted for this book. (Wayland Picture Library)

page 18 A photograph of Whitworth's lathe; hand-tinted for this book. (The Science Museum)

page 20 Babbage's 'difference machine'; hand-tinted for this book. (Ann Ronan Picture Library)

page 22 The trial of Richard Trevithick's single-cylinder locomotive 'Catch-me-who-can'; hand-tinted for this book. (Ann Ronan Picture Library)

page 24 An Albion Printing Press; hand-tinted for this book. (St. Bride Printing Library)

page 26 The front page from *Le Petit Journal* for 1 September 1907. (Ann Ronan Picture Library)

page 28 A portrait of Sir Joseph Whitworth. (Mary Evans Picture Library)

page 30 Otto's gas engine; tinted for this book. (Mary Evans Picture Library)

page 32 Bell's prototype telephone in operation; hand-tinted for this book. (Wayland Picture Library)

page 34 Sholes's first typewriter, made in 1872; hand-tinted for this book. (Wayland Picture Library)

page 36 An engraving from the *Petit Parisien* of 1894; tinted for this book. (Mary Evans Picture Library)

page 38 A Mergenthaler Linotype machine; hand-tinted for this book. (Mary Evans Picture Library)

page 40 A page from *The Illustrated London News* of 11 September 1926; hand-tinted for this book. (Wayland Picture Library)

page 42 An early X-ray machine of 1897; hand-tinted for this book. (Wayland Picture Library)

page 44 A pocket-sized camera of 1875; hand-tinted for this book. (Wayland Picture Library)

page 46 A Comet 4. (Dr. Alan Beaumont)

page 48 A Digital PDP 8 computer in use in the late 1960's; hand-tinted for this book. (Digital Equipment Co. Ltd.)

page 50 A combine harvester at work. (Massey Ferguson)

page 52 The fuelling machine at the nuclear power station at Sizewell. (Central Electricity Generating Board)

page 54 Robots on the production line at British Leyland's factory in Longbridge, Birmingham. (British Leyland)

Index